AF498392

THE OBJECTS OF TECHNOLOGY

AND

INDUSTRIAL MUSEUMS:

TWO LECTURES

ADDRESSED TO THE PHILOSOPHICAL INSTITUTION, EDINBURGH, IN FEBRUARY 1856,

BY GEORGE WILSON, M.D., F.R.S.E.,

REGIUS PROFESSOR OF TECHNOLOGY IN THE UNIVERSITY OF EDINBURGH, AND DIRECTOR OF THE
INDUSTRIAL MUSEUM OF SCOTLAND.

EDINBURGH:
SUTHERLAND AND KNOX, 60 SOUTH BRIDGE.
LONDON: SIMPKIN, MARSHALL, & CO.
MDCCCLVI.

Price Sixpence.

PREFACE.

THE Two Lectures occupying the following pages were addressed to the Philosophical Institution of Edinburgh, in the course of this spring. I gladly availed myself of the opportunity offered me by its Directors, to bring the subjects of which the Lectures treat before the large and intelligent audience which attends the evening meetings of that Institution. The Lectures were formally announced in connection with 'Granite and its Derivatives, including Glass, Porcelain, and Aluminium;' as the text, however, was but slenderly adhered to, it has not been repeated on thetitle-page.

Through the good offices of the editor of the EDINBURGH NEWS, these pages were circulated in his journal, and are now reprinted from its columns at a cost which makes the reprint accessible to most who will care to read it. I trust that its publication will serve to familiarise general readers with the name and nature of Technology, and will induce the Scottish people to press upon Government the great desirableness of steps being taken without delay to erect the promised Industrial Museum of Scotland, for which a site is purchased in Edinburgh, and specimens are being collected by me.

I will make no apology for referring those desiring further information on a subject of which I am as yet the only formal representative in the country, to an Inaugural Lecture—'What is Technology?' Sutherland & Knox, Edinburgh, 1855: to an Address—'On the Relations of Technology to Agriculture,' published in the 'Highland and Agricultural Society's Transactions' for March 1856: and to a paper 'On Pharmacy as a Branch of Technology,' published in the 'Pharmaceutical Journal' for April 1856.

G. W.

UNIVERSITY OF EDINBURGH,
April, 1856.

LECTURES ON TECHNOLOGY.

LECTURE I.—ON INDUSTRIAL SCIENCE.

I come before you for the first time as Professor Wilson; but a namesake of mine, one Dr George Wilson, who formerly lectured to you, has given me such assurance that you are a kindly and indulgent audience, that I am not afraid to try your patience. I need it the more, that you have the memory of your former president, the great Professor Wilson, to make you think little of any lesser Professor Wilson, and I have not only myself to introduce to you, but also a very shy protégé called 'Technology.' This mysterious entity has suddenly made its appearance amongst us, few know whence or how, and even the dictionaries reluctantly open their leaves to it. Technology is what the old Romans would have called '*insolens verbum*'—an unusual, an insolent, forward, or presuming word. No advertisement appeared in the newspapers announcing its expected advent; no gigantic rainbow-coloured bills upon the walls sought to accustom the eyes of the public to the terrible word; no human tortoises, bearing on breast and back defensive armour lettered with the mysterious title, walked meekly through the streets of Edinburgh, hoping by their lowly attitude to propitiate the astonished inhabitants towards the inexplicable symbol which they bore. The heralds did not proclaim it at the Cross; the Right Hon. the Lord Provost did not propose to confer upon it the freedom of the city; nor did cautionary paragraphs beseech Conservative philologists not to pledge themselves to the barbaric word, as a better term would solicit their suffrages before long. No! One day it made its appearance at I know not how many doors in the town, rang the bell, made the knocker thunder, darted in the moment the servant opened the door, and mounted the stairs as fast as it could climb. You were engaged at the time at your devotions, or hearing the children their lessons, or writing to your brother in the Crimea, or discussing with your lawyer the terms of your marriage-settlement, or your will, or

Mrs Jean was making her elder-flower wine,
And it's what brings the *word* at sic a like time.

No matter what; without wiping its feet on the mat, or so much as 'by your leave,' it invaded your privacy, insisted on shaking hands with you, and, as if certain that it would be a matter of unbounded delight, proclaimed in a foreign tongue that you were favoured with a visit from 'Technology.' I may be wrong in some particulars, as even the best historians occasionally are, but I leave you to judge whether or not I have given the generally credited account of the dark transaction under notice. Never-

theless, I am free to confess that I think it only a myth. The word is a stranger, but one of noble Greek lineage. It has long been honoured in the schools of science on the Continent. It has a dignified place in the Universities of France, Italy, and Germany. By them it was commended to acceptance in this country, and it soon won the regard of those who made its acquaintance. Before long it was presented to her Majesty, who was pleased to assign to it a chair of state, and to appoint me guardian of that chair.

Her Majesty as a Queen can do no wrong. Her Majesty as a woman loves to redress wrong; but neither as monarch nor woman has Lady Queen Victoria found anything to blame in the insolent word. Approved by her, it would be treason to condemn it; sanctioned by her, it is but courtesy to employ it. When a better word is suggested we shall adopt it. Till then, let us not quarrel with this one. The meaning of the word may be discovered without troubling Greek lexicons. We are familiar every one of us with the term 'technical,' as signifying what is peculiar to the practice of an art ('*techni*' or '*techno*'), and with '*logy*' as signifying doctrine or science. If, then, we put the words together we shall have technology, signifying 'the science or doctrine of the peculiar practices of the arts.' But as every piece of art-practice is peculiar, we may omit that qualifying term; and as art has no existence till it is practised, we may omit the word 'practice.' And the word 'science' will suffice without the synonyme 'doctrine,' so that we condense the translation of technology into 'the science of art;' but as it limits itself to utilitarian or economic art, it is better to say, 'the science of useful art, or of the useful arts.' If there be any objection on the score of euphony, dismiss the word technology as harsh in sound, and take in its place 'industrial science,' *i.e.*, the science, or fundamental laws, or guiding principles, or settled theory of the industrial arts. I will now try to illustrate the objects of technological or industrial science. To prevent myself from wandering too widely into purely general or abstract speculations, I have assigned myself the text of granite and its derivatives; but I will frankly confess at the outset that I have no intention of adhering very closely to my text; and that the syllabus is not to be held as binding upon me. I propose this evening, in addressing you as a general, not an academic or professional audience, to consider some of the chief objections, which an intelligent, earnest, and educated assemblage of religious men and women may justly oppose to the encouragement of industrial science; and in next evening's lecture to consider how a museum or collection of industrial objects may best serve the interests of mankind. I have purposely chosen a wide range of subject, in the hope that each section of the audience will find something to interest it in one or other of the topics discussed. I will not moralise largely as I proceed, but leave you to gather the lessons which such an exposition cannot fail to teach, especially these three :—First, How wonderful the properties are which God has conferred upon matter, and from moment to moment sustains in it. Second, How wonderful the powers are which He has conferred upon man, created in His image, who has been able to discover so many of these properties. Third, How manifold are the materials which, by human ingenuity, may be made serviceable in providing for the wants of man.

Our text, then, is GRANITE. Looked at from a technological point of view, it is paradoxically remarkable as at once the most enduring and the most perishable of rocks. One half of its industrial applications—the only one which we are to look at this evening—depends upon its enduringness ; the other—which will occupy us next evening—depends upon its perishableness.

No hills are more grand and picturesque than hills of granite. They lift their stately heads, as we see in the mountain-peaks of Arran, high up into the clear, cold air, and fear neither lightning nor storm. No hills better deserve the name which the Hebrew poets loved to give to mighty mountains—the everlasting hills. They are everlasting in the sense of enduring as compared with the duration of man or his works. In the lapse of 4000 years, nation after nation has been spoiled of the earthly immortality which it promised itself, and only relics more mournful than oblivion, reveal that it ever existed. Babylon has fallen, Nineveh is a heap of ruins, Thebes a city of mummies, Athens an eyeless skeleton, Rome an inhabited sepulchre, Jerusalem a thrice-ruined temple : all, so far as man made them, are but the spectral shadows of what they were ; but if a map of Arran had been made 4000 years ago, it would in all its great features represent what Arran is now. Nay, I think it not unlikely that if Noah could return among us, he might show us the very valley in Mount Ararat where the Ark rested. However that may be, if we look to Palestine, Greece, Italy, or Egypt, so far as their natural features are concerned, and compare the descriptions of them which have come down to us from remote times with the present condition of their best known regions, such as the Cataracts of the Nile, the mountains round Jerusalem, the hills about Athens or the neighbourhood of Rome, the difference is scarcely appreciable, provided we always exclude from consideration the effect of earthquakes and volcanoes, which is in truth exceptional, and that of man, which, after all, goes for very little.

The granite hills are everlasting also, as tried by standards which can find no place for a thing so fleeting as a generation of men. Napoleon told his soldiers in the plains of Egypt that forty centuries looked down on them from the summits of the Pyramids ; but the stones of the Pyramids, which are older by uncounted centuries than Adam, were not born when there were granite mountains hoary with age. And we may possibly form a faintly imperfect conception of the antiquity of some of those rocks, if we consider that in all probability more than one of the stars are younger than they. At all events, during incalculable periods they have gazed into the abysses of space ; and the mightiest, perhaps, of the events of the universe were not transacted till millions of years after those ancient monarchs first wore upon their brows their crowns of snow.

They are everlasting, finally, in the sense of renewing themselves in the only way created things can, namely by the birth of successive generations ; so that, whilst certain of the granite hills are unimaginably old, others have arisen from the fertile depths below within geologically recent times, and have witnessed at least the dawn of the historic period, and the last stages through which the earth passed before it was made ready for man.

But what have those relations of granite rocks to do with technology and industrial science ? They affect it thus. The enduringness of the granite mountains belongs to the blocks cut out of them, down even to the smallest fragments. No material, accordingly, is so suitable for buildings or erections which are to be very lasting. The air can rust nothing out of granite blocks ; rain can dissolve nothing out of them ; rivers even may flow in granite-beds for miles without ceasing to be soft—i.e., unimpregnated with saline matter. Frost has little power to split them ; their component particles are bound together by a strong cohesion ; plants do not readily grow on them ; they remain undiscoloured for ages. In proof of this, we have the obelisks of the ancient Egyptians, still standing like detached peaks of granite hills. Those obelisks, not only beneath the serene atmosphere of Egypt, but after transference to the capitals of Western and Northern Europe, display, uneffaced, unblunted even, the hieroglyphics which were cut upon them three thousand years ago. In the British Museum most present have probably seen granite sarcophagi and colossal figures, which might have come from the sculptor's hand yesterday. Those good qualities, however, are necessarily accompanied by a corresponding difficulty in quarrying and carving the stone, and thus a large demand is made on the ingenuity, enterprise, skill, and patience of the stone-cutter. Into this I will not minutely enter ; but you can readily understand that the employment of gunpowder to blast granite rocks ; the slow process of boring holes in them ; the tedious driving of wedges into these holes ; the rougher dressings by heavy hammers ; the sawings into slabs by great iron saws driven by steam ; the protracted polishing by moving the slabs over each other ; the employment of swift turning-lathes, and special iron tools, to give the last touches to curved surfaces—include a great technological domain, and involve a multitude of applications of science to art. The stone-mason of this country, the hewer and carver of these rugged, intractable, stubborn rocks, is, as Hugh Miller has shown us by precept and example, a very noble specimen of the industrial man, and all the more so that he too often falls a sacrifice to his hard labour, and dies young in years, having lived only long enough to carve his own tombstone. Let him be thoughtfully regarded as one of the hardest-wrought of hard-working men, whom industrial science hopes yet to save, by the substitution of machinery for bodily labour, from that slow self-murder which is too often inseparable from his calling. What the nature of his work is you will best appreciate by the records of our lighthouses. Our works on lighthouses are all delightful reading such as Smeaton's 'Record of the Building of the Eddystone Lighthouse,' the elder Stevenson's 'Record of the Building of the Bell Rock Light,' and his son Alan's very dramatic and picturesque description of the Lighthouse of Skerryvore. It is largely built of granite, and the modes of quarrying and fashioning that stone are incidentally but fully given in his work, and connected with the striking story of the building of the great northern beacon.

Turning aside from granite as a rock which we speak of as if it were uniform in structure, we have now to look at it as an aggregate of minerals. Its name signifies that it is. The word 'granite' implies made up of separate grains. There is no stone to which the name, as a name, might not be given ; but it is specially applied to the one rock, because its component grains are very different in colour and lustre, and catch the eye of even the most casual observer. In the best known, the most typical, and, as it were, leading granite (of which there are many varieties), the component grains are of three different kinds. There are never fewer than two; in reality there are always more than even three, but beyond three we find only rarely disseminated and irregularly scattered grains.

The first of the three grains which concern us most this evening are transparent, often quite colourless, and very like glass. They consist of rock-crystal, otherwise called quartz.

The second are to appearance opaque, black, or rather dark-brown, and possess a peculiar silvery or pearly glitter (in Latin, *micare*), from which power to glisten their constituent is named mica.

The third grains are opaque, resemble white marble, and are white, cream-coloured, buff, flesh-coloured, or red. Their material is called felspar; *i.e.*, feld (German), or field spar, a spar abounding in the fields. On the felspar the colour of granite depends.

As regards size, they may be no larger than grains of sand or sugar, or as large as currants. All may be about the same size, or one kind of grain larger than the others. Any one may be in crystals many inches, or even feet in length. In 1725, a cave opened at Zinkenberg, on the Grimsel, contained five tons of crystal, among which were columns, clear as water, from 500 to 800 lbs. In 1770, in Hagdorn, near Fischbach, a column weighing 14 cwt., one 8 cwt., and one 6 cwt., were found, of the greatest purity.

As for the shape of the grains, they are generally squeezed together in the rock, which was once probably liquid. But they often shoot into crystals, that is, solids with plane or flat sides or faces, bounded or circumscribed by definite angles. Rock-crystal or quartz appears as a six-sided prism and pyramid; mica as a rhomboid, or solid with six lozenge faces; felspar occurs as an oblique prism.

Rock-crystal is the characteristic ingredient of glass; felspar, the characteristic source of the constituent of earthenware and porcelain; mica is of much less importance.

Rock-crystal is called also silica, from the Latin word for a flint, which has the same composition as quartz. It is known as a crystalline solid; as a white, glistering, gritty powder, and as a soft impalpable one. An intense heat melts it, but no heat can volatilise it, and it is insoluble in all ordinary fluids. It consists of oxygen, and a combustible body, in some respects like charcoal, in others like a metal, called silicon or silicium.

A beautiful and most interesting department of technology is connected with rock-crystal, as one of the precious stones or gems. It is the chief element of glass, and the largest constituent of porcelain, and we shall look to it again in its relation to these; but before we consider it as transformed by man in the course of his industrial doings into marvellous things, it must be looked at in connection with an art which perhaps some may be jealous of hearing called utilitarian. Rock-crystal is one of the precious stones or gems, and is pre-eminent among them in a threefold way—1. It is itself ranked among 'the stones most precious.' 2. It is the chief ingredient of many of those most highly prized which contain other things besides itself. 3. It is associated with the larger number of the gems as these are with granite. I wish to refer specially to the precious stones, that, in connection with them as famous and familiar things, I may dispose of two weighty objections to technology, and may urge an important argument in defence of its study and practice.

Mankind in all ages have looked upon those few minerals, which they have called precious stones, gems, or jewels, with delight and wonder. Their origin has been ascribed to supernatural causes, and they have been invested with the most mysterious powers. They could render their wearer invisible; they could banish drunkenness (especially the amethyst), cure madness, and make certain the passionate love of those who were objects of affection. They could detect poison, and were its best antidotes; they could heal, indeed, all diseases. In darkness they shone with a light of their own, bright as that of the sun, but bright, nevertheless, with an unearthly splendour. By all nations they were accounted as things regal and sacred, to be employed in the adornment of great kings and queens, and dedicated to the service of God. And if their employment was not restricted to such purposes, they were at least kept apart from ordinary uses. The songs and legends and fairy tales of all peoples are full of references to them, and the poets never wearied of comparing them to the rainbow and the azure sky, to flowers, and to stars. Even in these utilitarian and technological days, how much poetry lurks under the word 'gem.' We call a precious stone a gem. The word signifies literally a 'bud or flower,' and most happily denotes those crystals which shoot up and bud forth from their stony beds with forms as graceful, though of a different type of symmetry, and with colours as varied and as gorgeous as those of flowers. The amethysts, emeralds, garnets, and topazes are the true flowers of the granite, not the insignificant lichens which the botanist alone counts as belonging to the granitic Flora. Well, then, could not technology spare those unfading flowers to the poet? Has any but a jeweller an interest in knowing how diamonds are cut with lead wheels by patient Dutchmen? or how ingenious Germans convert, by chemical processes, common pebbles into choice carnelians and onyxes, or how clever Brazilians change yellow into red topazes? Because, in these later days, there has arisen a Sir Humphry Davy with a wonderful lamp, are we to forget Aladdin and his more wonderful lamp, and the trees he saw loaded thick with emeralds and rubies? or because the Queen had to send a great army and take a mighty Indian fort before she could get her Koh-i-noor diamond, are we to lose sight of the simple way in which Sinbad's friends the merchants procured their sackfuls of the biggest gems from the Valley of Diamonds? Now, I am not about to tire you with an account of jewellers' work, which, in truth, we have no time to consider. Accepting the protest which we have heard against the flowers of the crystal world being regarded as mere substitutes for money, or useful because they can be converted into pretty studs and buttons, or clasps and brooches, and the heads of pins; and remembering that the same protest is made against every branch of industrial science, I wish to consider the two cardinal objections that are made to the modern zealous encouragement of utilitarian art as compared with the ancient mere sufferance of it. The one objection is, that our modern utilitarianism is stealing from us our imaginations; the other and more serious objection, is, that it is killing our consciences.

It is contended, then, that in these days the spirit of utilitarianism has so possessed the minds of the people that all interest is likely to be lost in imaginative art. The true object of technology, it is said, if you translate the word into plain English, is how to answer most sumptuously the questions, 'What shall we eat?' and 'What shall we drink?' and 'Wherewithal shall we be clothed?' and the only fine arts it fosters are those which increase the sensual comforts and gratify the vanity of that luxurious animal man. The spirit, too, of its teaching is affirmed to be, that the money-value of an object is the true criterion of its worth to the world. A diamond is worth much gold, and therefore to be esteemed. It is also a good thing for cutting glass with, and indispensable to window-makers, but it may be left to fantastic Orientals to call it a Mountain of Light. Now, it is not to be denied that there is in our day a disposition among ourselves and the other active nations of the world to encourage utilitarianism as a thing most deserving encouragement, and that, though this may not be done in the spirit of depreciating other things worthy of being fostered, these suffer by its exaltation. But who is to blame for this? Not the utilitarian, I think! It is assumed in the argument against him, that the world in former ages paid sufficient attention to utilitarianism, but that now it is paying too much. But this is begging the entire question in dispute; for when was the world too industrial, and when did the fine arts gain by men being idle and miserable? The utilitarian does no more than declare that bread for the hungry, water for the thirsty, clothing for the naked, and homes for the houseless can be furnished to all, if men will but wisely use their faculties, and conquer that physical world which was given them to conquer. If it be desirable, as assuredly it is, that after being fed, and clothed, and housed, they should cultivate their imaginations, let the poet and his brother artists look to that. Hungry, thirsty, ragged wretches are not the audiences who weep over Tennyson's 'Maud,' or crowd to hear Jenny Lind sing, or make pilgrimages to London to visit the picture galleries. To feed, to clothe, to house the needy, are surely not acts which involve any invasion of their imaginations. If the poet, and the painter, and the sculptor, and the musician, will go before and go beside, and follow after the utilitarian, they will find him in no case an enemy, and in most cases a friend; and if they will not do their work, they should not complain that it is left undone.

In reality, the question whether utilitarianism shall or shall not prevail against non-utilitarian fine art, depends upon a matter beyond human control, namely, whether there shall be more great artists or great utilitarians given to the world within a particular epoch. Let a Shakspere be born, and he will make his nation imaginative, and keep it so for centuries after his death. Let a Bacon be born, and he will make his nation utilitarian and keep it so for centuries after his death. Let both adorn the same epoch, and that epoch will reflect the spirit of both, as the last two hundred years have done. And so long as a Shakspere and a Bacon, a Milton and a Newton, a James Watt and a Walter Scott, a Davy and a Byron, a John Herschel and a Thomas Campbell, a Faraday and a Tennyson, are given us together, the world will find no difficulty in being at the same time utilitarian and poetical. If it shall ever please Providence to send us no poets, then we must grow unpoetical, and the faster the better. And if it shall ever please Providence to send us no utilitarians, then we must at least grow non-utilitarian, though perhaps not become more poetical, only this time the slower the better. Let no one, then, quarrel with utilitarianism for being utilitarian. You might as well quarrel with a ball for being round. If poetry threatens to suffer, let the poets defend it from wrong.

There is one respect, however, in which I think too great a devotion to utilitarianism is doing mischief. An endeavour is being made to indoctrinate children with what is called useful knowledge, to the exclusion of fairy tales and other so-called useless imaginative literature. I have no sympathy with this. It is wrong in principle, and wrong in policy. The childhood of an infant, like the childhood of a nation, is a time when the imagination is the great inlet to knowledge, and it should be allowed to remain so. The poet is entitled to the childhood of every man and woman. The utilitarian may touch the finger-tips of the youth, and often may entirely clasp the hand of the man; but the child is as useless to him as his knowledge is useless to the child. I count it, for example, an unwise and even a cruel thing to tell a wondering child that a diamond is not a fairy marvel, but only so much black soot or charcoal. The fact has no interest for a child. It is, indeed, beyond its comprehension, and to the small extent that it is apprehended it can only occasion perplexity. Tell a child, if it must be spoken to on the matter, that a diamond is so much sunlight condensed and crystallised, and you may enlarge its conception of that exquisite gem without misleading it. For, in a sense which the greatest philosophers would acknowledge to be a just one, a diamond is so much imprisoned sunlight; and if you burn the diamond you can set the light free again. On such a conception a child's mind can lay hold, and grasp it as it grows older better and better, till by-and-bye it learns to qualify it by the added idea of a ponderable solid embodying the imponderable light, and so gives wings to the chrysalis thought. I am not objecting to teaching children utilitarian facts, but to teaching such facts so as to cripple the imagination and morbidly develop or distract the intellect. A dwarfed and chilled imagination will help no one to study or to work. The boy who is greatly interested in 'Aladdin's Wonderful Lamp' is sure, by-and-bye, to be greatly interested in all the wonderful safety lamps, electric lamps, and self-lighting lamps of Davy and his successors; and I have noticed that all my schoolfellows who have since distinguished themselves as men of thought or action, were great story-readers in their early days.

I wash my hands free, as Professor of Technology, of any approval of the so-called intellectual style of teaching. I have listened, on occasion, by request, to the uttered wisdom of little girls, who told me that the specific gravity of gold is 19·5; that the proper name of salt is chloride of sodium, and that the animal kingdom is divided into Mammalia, Aves, Reptilia, and Pisces: all which I heard with suppressed groans. The knowledge was good of its kind, but did the child no good. It was furnished as mental fuel, and had been shovelled into the child's head with intent that it should take fire, and warm and light up its whole being; and it would have done so, had it been laid on the hearth of its imagination, where a fire is ever burning; but instead thereof, it had been cast into the unlighted furnace of the intellect, which it had only choked. So far is it from being the intention of scientific utilitarianism or technology to encourage such a style of teaching, to rob children of their imaginations and distract their intellects, that one of its great aims—an aim with which personally I sympathise deeply—is by lessening the toil and trouble which the great majority of mankind are compelled to spend, even from their earliest years, in gaining their bread, to give them leisure and -opportunity to feed their imaginations and cultivate their intellects as God intended they should do. Let no poet or painter, then, or artist of any other kind, or friend {or lover of these or of the arts, think unkindly of utilitarian technology. It can do them no harm, if they are true to themselves, and it will be their fault if it do not render them service.

I will not affirm that there are no grounds for the charge that utilitarianism has made men sordid and worldly. Great discoveries of gold diggings; ready access through the medium of swift steamers and railways to the choicest regions of the earth; the command which the telegraph gives over the markets of the world; the immense improvements in machinery; the new, and newer, and newest applications of chemistry to the useful arts; the great advances of agriculture, of navigation, of the art of war, and the wide diffusion of knowledge among the people, have unquestionably a strong tendency to fix men's thoughts too much upon this world, and make them forget how soon they must leave it.

All this is true; but for the evil, industrialism is not to blame. We are at best but narrow-minded creatures, troubled to carry more than one idea in our heads at a time, and but partially able to keep hold of two worlds at once. By all means let moralists and Christian divines, and every good man and woman, warn their brethren against mistaking this little passing world for the great eternal one. But to abolish industrialism would not cure the evil, and industrialism has many evils to cure. Its vocation far more is to relieve the wants of the poor than to minister to the luxuries of the rich; and we have the poor with us always.

Think how many thousands of starving men there are in our country at this moment for whom there is bread enough and to spare in this God's world of ours, if wisdom and patience were allowed their perfect work! Think how many women crowd our streets, forlorn outcasts for whom no man cares, who have been driven to perdition of soul and body by those quite vulnerable demons—Cold and Hunger! And think, lastly, how many stalwart working men and patient house mothers there are who, though not starving, are yet so overworked, so insufficiently fed and clothed, that they will be aged at fifty, and retain only vitality sufficient to rot slowly away in workhouses till they fall into their graves.

Think of this woful multitude of sufferers and sinners whom the miseries of their bodies daily drive into the commission of terrible crimes, and judge whether industrial science can wrong religion by feeding, and clothing, and healing, and employing so inglorious an army of unwilling martyrs to the cause of imperfect civilisation!

Wealth and luxury are assuredly not less fruitful parents of crime than poverty and hunger, and if the criminals are fewer, they are often all the blacker, and they are few only because riches and leisure cannot be the endowment of many. But industrial science is as little responsible for the crimes of the rich as for the crimes of the poor. The fault of both is, that they are not industrial. The poor cannot work; the rich will not work; and both pay the penalty of idleness, which, whether voluntary or involuntary, is always punished in a world of which the law is Labour.

I think, then, that industrialism is no enemy of religion. I believe that it is most ready to be its handmaid. But let me add that, in itself industrial science is neither religious nor irreligious. It is simply embodied power innocent of either good or evil intentions; as ready to make gunpowder as to make chloroform; as willing to cast iron into bomb-shells as into household grates; and no more interested in distilling an elixir of life than in concentrating the most subtle poison.

The often quoted declaration of Bacon, that 'knowledge is power,' is especially true in reference to industrial science, if you take the aphorism without any qualification. Knowledge is power, and only power. It is not love; it is not hate; it is not virtue; it is not vice; it is not mercy; it is not justice; and least of all is it revenge. It has not a soft touch or a gentle look, a kind heart or a pitying ear. It has only a clear eye and a strong hand. Its symbol is the steam-hammer, to which it is equally indifferent, whether it is forging shapeless iron into goodly merchant ships, or crushing goodly merchant ships into shapeless iron. Industrial science is thus as free to the religious as to the irreligious, and is alike the blind instrument of both. Whether it shall produce evil or good depends on those by whom it is guided, and the business of the Christian is not to flee from it, as Moses at first fled from his wonder-working rod, because it put on the aspect of the subtle, terrible, malignant serpent, but to stretch forth his hand and take it, and hold it up before men as a sceptre which, wisely used, will compel the earth to obey the will of God.

I trust, then, that I may rely upon the sympathy and assistance of all good men and women, and upon these all the more the better they are, towards my Chair of Technology and the Industrial Museum of Scotland. I would compare industrial technology to one of the tribes of Israel, among which the Land of Promise was divided. I would not compare it to the lion-like Judah, or to Benjamin the ravening wolf, or to Naphtali the hind let loose, or to Dan the biting serpent, or to Joseph the fruitful bough, but to the lowliest of them all, who, you will remember, is thus described:—'Issachar is a strong ass couching down between two burdens: and he saw that rest was good and the land that it was pleasant; and bowed his shoulder to bear, and became a servant unto tribute.' This Issachar, the strong and patient, peaceful bearer of burdens, and servant of his brethren, is the very symbol of industrial science, and he can bear two burdens, so that you need not be afraid to lay one upon him, an injunction which I should be glad you understood on the present occasion, as signifying that you cannot by your gifts overload the shelves of the Industrial Museum.

And now, having in a long digression disposed of two grave questions affecting my subject, let me announce the positive truth which I seek to connect with the topic before us:—I was referring to rock crystal as connected with a peculiarly interesting department of technology. 1. As itself a precious stone. 2. As a prominent ingredient of those gems which contain other things besides itself. 3. As occurring along with those most prized.

There are two famous gems, indeed, perhaps the most famous of all, which are not included among the children of the granite. The one is a choice gift to us from the plant world, viz., the diamond. The flowers have kept the secret of its production to themselves, but they have whispered enough to let it appear that to them we are indebted for that rare crystal most akin to the light, without which no plant can open its buds or perfect its flowers. The other exceptional gem, the pearl, comes to us from the animal world, and its subdued moon-like splendour, as contrasted with the sun-like diamond, is no unbefitting symbol of the smaller dependence of animals than of plants on the light of day.

The remaining precious stones are literally stones, the offspring of the rock, and of the earth, earthy. Take for example those mentioned in the Bible, without stopping to question whether or not the names are rightly rendered by our translators, seeing that it is only with the names we have at present to do.

In Aaron's breastplate there were twelve stones, namely, a sardius (or ruby), a topaz, and a carbuncle, an emerald, a sapphire, and a diamond, a ligure (or opal), an agate, and an amethyst, a beryl, an onyx, and a jasper.—(Exod. xxviii. 17.)

In St John's description of the Heavenly City we read of twelve foundations—jasper, sapphire, chalcedony, emerald, sardonyx, sardius (or ruby), chrysolite, beryl, topaz, chrysoprasus, jacinth, amethyst; 'and the twelve gates were twelve pearls, every several gate was of one pearl.'—(Rev. xxi. 19-21.)

Now, omitting the diamond and pearl, and counting no stone twice, we have sixteen gems. But of these no fewer than one half, namely, agate, amethyst, chalcedony, chrysoprasus, jasper, onyx, opal (ligure), sardonyx, are slight modifications of silica. Some, like the amethyst, are coloured crystallised rock-crystal; the others more resemble silica in the form of flint; but all agree in consisting almost entirely of that most abundant and common earthy or mineral matter, which, as forming the smooth milk-white pebbles of our Highland brooks, we distinguish in our vernacular by the contemptuous name of chucky-stones (stones to be chucked about); which, as forming the sand upon our sea shores, we count the very type of useless barrenness; and of which, in its shape of sandstone, we build our rudest walls and meanest erections.

The whole of the precious stones in question are, in truth, only coloured sandstones. Nor is there anything rare in the source of their colour. A little iron rust, a little manganese, a little coaly matter, or a few scales of mica, are sufficient to give them their beautiful tints. And the most beautiful, perhaps, of all the siliceous gems, the precious opal (of which there exists a piece at Vienna, weighing 1 lb., valued at L.40,000), if it owe its splendid blaze of colours to anything but its structure, owes it only to the presence of a little water.

Of the other eight stones, three—the ruby, the carbuncle, and the sapphire—are identical. The ruby and carbuncle are exactly so, and the sapphire differs only in colour from them. A ruby or carbuncle may be called a red sapphire, or a sapphire may be called a blue ruby. They consist of the same thing as the emery powder with which we clean rusty needles, and it is the same thing as the earth of clay, alumina. The rarest azure-blue sapphire, or blazing ruby, is only crystallised coloured clay-earth.

Of the remaining five stones, two—the emerald and the beryl — are but different names for one thing. They are largely made up of flint-earth (silica), and clay-earth (alumina), and their colour is owing to an abundant metal, chromium. They do contain, however, one comparatively rare body called glucina, the oxide of an unfamiliar metal. Yet there is nothing remarkable in the appearance of this body, which is a white powder resembling closely flint-earth and clay-earth, and only occasionally found forming a gem. For it is only a few among the beryls that are sufficiently beautiful to be counted among precious stones, and fine emeralds are so rare that a single one (no doubt a large one) at Vienna is valued at L.50,000.

The last three stones are the chrysolite, the topaz, and the jacinth. The chrysolite is made up largely of the continually recurring flint-earth, silica; its rather unattractive yellowish or olive-green colour results from the presence of a little iron rust; and what is not siliceous or ferruginous in it is the uncostly substance magnesia. The topaz is, again, clay-earth and flint-earth, with the addition of a common body, fluorine.

At length, however, in the last of the sacred gems, we encounter one constituted of very rare materials. The jacinth is composed of the least common materials of all the gems. It has in it an earth called zirconia, the oxide of a metal which occurs very sparingly in any part of the crust of the globe. This forms two-thirds of it, the other third is silica. Of all the gems it is probably the least known, and the least prized. Most of those present, I suppose, never saw it. It is a brown stone, of no remarkable beauty, resembling a red-brown garnet, which is often sold as a jacinth or hyacinth. The rarest of the gems is thus the least prized of them all.

There are other precious stones besides those which I have named; but they all consist of common things. The garnet, for example, the spinelle-ruby, and lapis-lazuli or ultramarine, are compounds of the ever reappearing silica, alumina, magnesia, and iron oxide; the splendid colour of ultramarine (which we are able to imitate artificially), depending, in addition to these materials, on the presence of sulphur and soda.

The turquoise is clay-earth united with bone-earth (phosphate of lime), coloured by oxide of copper. Many turquoises are fragments of fossil bones stained with copper. Malachite is a very common copper ore. Satin spar and Derbyshire spar, besides other prized spars, consist chiefly of lime. Jet is coal, and amber is petrified rosin. In short, with the exception of the dull brown jacinth and the emerald, the great majority of precious stones are only coloured sand, flint, clay-earth, or clay, whilst the diamond is charcoal, and the pearl chalk.

If any I address hear this for the first time, I can well imagine them saying, ' For us hitherto a diamond was a diamond and a pearl a pearl; the sapphire the embodied azure of the sky; and the emerald the green which the earth loves in spring. But now, much apparently to your contentment, they are turned into soot and chalk, and clay, and iron rust!'

Now, I sympathise greatly with the feeling which leads to this protest. I have pleaded that children should not too early be despoiled of their romantic beliefs. And there are grown-up children of the best sort, who keep the hearts of children, in manly or womanly breasts, even to extreme old age, and who, I should be glad, could believe all their days, that diamonds were crystallised May-dew, and pearls the tears of mermaids, and sapphires chips from the vault of heaven, and emeralds leaves of the trees that grew in Eden. But to most of us, as even to a Wordsworth, the time irrevocably comes, when the fairy gleams of childhood fade into the light of common day; and we are all the descendants of her who ate of the fruit of the tree of knowledge of good and of evil, and must taste, like her, the bitter as well as the sweet; but the bitter here is a wholesome one. Why should we admire a diamond the less because a chemist can roast it into a cinder or burn it into choke-damp? Why should a pearl be pronounced unbeautiful because any one can rival the wanton Cleopatra, who changed one into a hateful draught by dissolving it in vinegar?

There is something unconsciously atheistic, materialistic, and barbaric in the notion that the rarity of its material is the chief element in the beauty of a beautiful object. All that the marble contributes to the beauty of the Apollo Belvidere, or the Medicean Venus, or any of the other statues that enchant the world, may be subtracted, without subtracting more than a fraction of their beauty; and that fraction makes the marble statue more beautiful than the plaster cast or the clay model, not because marble is rarer than plaster or clay, but simply because it is more beautiful. If the diamond had organised itself out of some unique and precious kind of matter, which alone, of all kinds of matter in the universe, could form it, then all praise to the self-made diamond! But if omnipotent hands carved it out of the most common, most unlikely, and most intractable materials, then, whilst the diamond is none the less beautiful, all the more honour redounds to its wonderful Carver. It might have been the law of nature that graceful shapes and gorgeous colours should have been found attached only to the rarest materials; as gold, for example, is a rare thing, as well as a very beautiful thing. But the law of nature is exactly the opposite. There is not, I am sure, a more beautiful object than a soap-bell, none which a youthful Shakspere or Milton is more likely to have tried his creative hand at producing. No flower or precious stone excels it in symmetry. None equals it in colour, and yet it is but a distended drop of muddy water. The secret of its beauty lies in its workmanship, and the same law applies to all created things.

This is the lesson I am anxious to enforce. It is, I will not say, a childish, but it is a childlike fancy to expect to find beautiful objects constructed out of a rare material, which by its very nature confers beauty upon all that is made of it. When we become men, and put away childish things, what we do find in the physical universe, are materials the most common, but workmanship the most rare. Herein lies a great argument, little appreciated, for man being a worker. Herein lies a justification of Industrial Museums, and a divine warrant for Chairs of Technology. Thus the material of the gems is the cheapest and rudest. To judge from the condition of the mass of this material at the earth's surface, its tendency is to assume ungraceful and dull-coloured forms. The clay or flint, or chalk or charcoal, does not help the artist, but must be subdued into beauty, and etherealised by him. It is susceptible of being made beautiful, and does not refuse to be beautified; but it is shy and coy, and reluctantly submits to be glorified. Not till it is touched by the finger of God does it start into shapes and hues of beauty; but how surpassingly beautiful they are! The crystallised gems are modelled into figures so perfect, that the mathematician wonders at their almost ideal symmetry. Some, like Sal-Gem, are exquisitely-squared cubes. The jacinth rises in four-angled campanile-like towers; the emerald in stately six-sided obelisks; the amethyst in twelve-sided cathedral-like spires; the diamond assumes a most symmetrical shape, like that of a doubled Egyptian pyramid; the topaz inclines obliquely, like the leaning Tower of Pisa; the garnet, the most many-sided of them all, shows twelve or twenty-four polished facets; and the pearl (which is not, however, a crystal), as it were, rounds these off, and grows into a perfect sphere. Each can assume many shapes, but all related, all beautiful, and so unaltering that their bounding angles do not vary.

Those crystals, in virtue of their structure, not their material, can influence nearly all the great forces of nature. They can transmit rays of light, and reflect them, bend them aside, break them in two, make them visible or invisible, and strangely change all their properties. They can similarly affect the rays of heat. They develop and modify electrical agencies. They act, and are acted on, like magnets, and when traversed by light, heat, electricity, and magnetism, display inner marvels of structure unsuspected till these forces revealed them.

I will say nothing of their colours, for these are familiar to you, nor enumerate further their characters. Enough has been said to show that they are among the most perfectly beautiful things that God has given us to delight our senses and imaginations, and to quicken our intellects; and yet they are made of the most common, most vulgar, and most worthless ingredients, and owe their graces solely to the exquisite skill with which those despised ingredients have been moulded, and carved, and tinctured with the choicest dyes. And they are bright with a lesson as heaven-born as themselves.

We are placed in a world where all are commanded to live by labour, the labour of head or hand, or heart or brain, or of all together. And lest we should be discouraged by the apparent intractability and meanness of the dull physical materials with which we must work, and should complain that we have to deal with a hard taskmaster, who sets us to make bricks but gives us no straw, behold He has stooped like a benignant father to His wilful children, and with His own Almighty hands has wrought into shapes of beauty the clay and sand and trodden dust beneath our feet. We are too apt to regard it as altogether exceptional that God should have shown to Moses on the mount patterns of all the things he should make for the service of the Tabernacle; we forget that He has in all ages given to men patterns of the way in which they should fashion the materials he has placed in their hands. And do not forget that it is not merely a few budlike gems that show this. The everlasting mountains, the plains, the valleys, the river-beds, and the caverns of the sea, are built up or hewn out of the same common things. All the might and grandeur of the ocean, whether as shown in its waves or in its icebergs, those mightiest of emeralds, sapphires, and diamonds, depend upon the most common of material things. All the splendours of the sky have a similar origin. All the trees of the forest, the meadow-grasses, and every fruit and flower, are but new forms of the same endlessly alterable materials; and the creatures of the whole animal kingdom, up to the highest models of manly and womanly beauty, are only the same things in other shapes. On every side we hear one great truth uttered from earth, and air, and sea, and sky, and plant, and animal—*The material is nothing, the workmanship is everything.* On their testimony I rest my case. They are the justifiers of industrial science. They furnish an argument for cheerful, hearty work, which may not before have fully struck you. To two alone of its aspects I will now refer.

In the first place, the infinite susceptibility of useful and beautiful modification which the most common things possess, assures us that, though we are not omnipotent, and cannot avail ourselves to more than a small extent of this susceptibility, yet we can largely turn it to account in our capacity as workmen; neither need we fear that all the generations of men to the end of time will exhaust the latent properties of even one kind of matter.

In the second place, as if not to deter us from work by showing us unapproachable examples of his power, it has pleased the Almighty worker to restrain His skill, if I may use such language, and whilst He has made all material things beautiful, to make none perfect.

Exquisitely graceful, for example, as crystals are, perfect crystals never occur. A faultless cube we do not see. Equilateral triangles or right angles, rigidly such, as tested mathematically, are not found, or facets unerringly plane. Poets speak of entire and perfect chrysolites, but crystallographers never saw them, and mathematicians never measured them.

It shows, as has been most justly urged by a profound thinker, how much greater man's intellect is than his senses, that we should have an unfaltering belief in the existence of such things as cubes and triangles, and circles, although we never saw them (*i.e.* perfect) and cannot produce them. But the conclusion I wish to draw from this curious fact is simply that on our globe the beauty of everything is as it were veiled and subdued, and for this among other reasons, that we may not be disheartened in working, by seeing the Divine ideal too perfectly realised before us.

And so, if our work never contents us, and, least of all, our best work, let us not seek a lower ideal, or be too despondent, still less throw our tools away in despair.

The workman's song, whether successful or not, should ever be, ' Excelsior!' the motto, ' Higher! higher!' We must postpone the thought of perfection till we stand before Him who can make us perfect, and our work too.

LECTURE II.—ON INDUSTRIAL MUSEUMS.

In last lecture special reference was made to the enduringness of granite, and the relation of that enduringness to industrial science. We are now to consider this rock as very perishable, and as yielding by its decay materials for important arts, and, in particular, for three, namely, the arts of the glass-maker, of the potter, and of the metal-worker, of which, however, I can discuss scarcely more than the first.

With a view to understand this, let us look again at the three minerals in ordinary granite. They are, as we have seen, the dark, glimmering, scaly mica; the glass-like quartz, which, when violet, we call amethyst, when yellow, cairngorm or false topaz; and the marble-like felspar, which appears of so rich a red in Peterhead and Egyptian granite.

The same Hebrew poets who loved to call the mountains everlasting also tell us that 'the perpetual hills bow down.' They do so in the sense of bending their heads, in the course of ages, to the blast, and wearing away under the storms of millenniums, slowly corroded by the air, dissolved by the rain, ploughed by the glacier, split by the frost, shivered by the lightning, and by all consumed into dust. They also bow their heads, in the sense of abasing themselves; and as they originally rose from the lower depths of the earth, often sink again into them. Those great physical agencies which, suddenly and, as it were, spasmodically exerted, produce, under our eyes, earthquakes and volcanoes, more slowly and silently exercised, lift entire continents to immense elevations, and build them up as mountain-chains; and again those agencies reverse their work, and the mountain-chains are buried 'deeper than plummet ever sounded.' But in so sinking, they are at length, in the majority of cases, plunged beneath the sea, and there are, of necessity, exposed to all the wear and tear of its waves, to the ebb and flow of its tides, to the fierce collision of rocks broken from themselves dashed wildly against them, to the grinding action of fragments of those rocks furrowing their surfaces, to the abrading contact of sand reducing them to its own likeness, and to the disintegrating influence of water soaking into every pore, and dissolving ingredients essential to their stability, till they are broken into pieces, worn into pebbles, ground into sand, and degraded into mud.

In this way the most ancient of the granite-rocks of the world have, in the remotest geological ages, utterly perished, and their relics, strangely altered, are all that remain to us. Those relics, sifted and sorted by the action of the waves, have afterwards been built up again beneath the sea into coherent masses, have been consolidated by pressure, have been hardened and, as it were, baked and semi-fused by subterraneous fire, and, torn and twisted by volcanic forces, have been lifted again to the surface, so as to form anew what we creatures of a day call everlasting hills.

Among those re-made rocks, I notice, and that simply in passing, that the mica of the granite is found predominating in certain of the stones which can be split into roof-slabs and floor-slabs; that the quartz forms sandstones, such as we prefer in this city and neighbourhood for building with; and that the felspar changes into those clay-stones which, when easily split, form our finest roofing-slates, and, when more compact, our flagstones or pavements.

Now, leaving unconsidered mica altogether, and passing without further reference from the consideration of the slates and sandstones as building materials, let us look at sand, i.e., ground-down quartz, as the basis of glass; and at clay, i.e., disintegrated felspar, as the chief constituent of pottery, and the source of the metal aluminium. Before doing so, however, let me notice that certain even of the more recent granites are so prematurely perishable, that they waste away even under serene atmospheres, and crumble down so swiftly where other granites show no signs of decay, that the continental geologists gravely refer to them as 'diseased granites.' It is from them that our finest porcelain clay is derived, so important an ingredient in pottery. First, however, of glass.

Pliny has a pleasant story of certain Phœnician sailors accidentally discovering the mode of making glass, by kindling, on a sandy river-bank, a fire to heat their cooking-vessels. These, for want of better supports, were rested upon lumps of natron, that is, crystallised carbonate of soda, such as is found at the present day in many parts of the world. The effect of the fire, as the story goes, was to melt the sand and soda into glass. But the story is incredible, for natron, under a slight heat, dissolves in the water which its crystals contain, and the fire must have been extinguished long before the sand and soda melted; nor is it easy to understand how an open fire could yield heat sufficient in any circumstances to effect their fusion. But the legend, doubtless, is founded in truth. Mankind probably first learned how to produce glass from striking incidental phenomena unexpectedly brought under their notice. Among such phenomena special prominence may be assigned to the effect of discharges of lightning in reducing the most refractory minerals to the condition of clear glass; to the effect of great casual conflagrations in reducing portions of buildings to vitreous masses; and perhaps, most of all, to the effect of the prolonged heat of furnaces, in causing the ashes of the fuel burned in them to glaze the stones or bricks of their walls and floors, and in fusing the calcined dross or scoriæ of metallic ores into slag, i.e., opaque glass.

Such phenomena must more or less have awakened the interest and attention of even rude workers, since fires were first lighted; and in all probability the ancient arts of the baker, potter, and blacksmith were not long practised before the dwellers in widely distant regions of the globe had learned the first principles of glass-making. It is thus, in all likelihood, one of the oldest of the arts. It is, at all events, a very old one, for we know, from drawings in the Egyptian tombs, and from objects found in them, that 2000 years B.C. expert glass-blowers abounded in Egypt.

The word glass is perhaps derived from the Latin word for ice, 'glacies,' from which we derive our words glacial and glacier; but this is uncertain. The thing itself is very familiar to all of us, though probably most would be puzzled to define or describe it. Its only synonyme is crystal, and this term may connect it with rock crystal or silica, which is the largest constituent of all the ordinary kinds of glass. The most remarkable thing, however, about glass is not its materials, but, as in the precious stones, its workmanship; and in the full sense of the word, as understood by natural philosophers, glass signifies a solid body possessing a peculiar structure, not a peculiar composition. In other words, it is the mode in which its particles are arranged together, not the nature of its particles, which makes glass, glass.

To render this clear, let it be observed that (setting aside plants and animals, the forms and structures of which are foreign to our present inquiry), three quite unlike external shapes and internal arrangements of particles are found in solids. These three are not the only kinds of form and structure found characterising dead matter, but they are the three most striking which prevail in those solids which have not formed parts of living beings. They are as follows :—1. Some solids are crystalline in shape and structure ; 2. Some are glassy or vitreous ; 3. Some are neither crystalline nor glassy, and are called amorphous, *i.e*, formless or shapeless, but the adjective also includes the idea of their being structureless. Glass is intermediate in character between a crystalline substance and an amorphous one, and it is rather unfortunate that one kind of glass should be called ' crystal,' which it is, however, only as resembling colourless quartz in hardness and transparency, not in shape or in structure, seeing that it is essential to good glass not to possess the properties of any crystal, but certain quite different properties. Let us very briefly consider wherein the difference lies. A crystal, such as the six-sided pyramid of quartz, or the eight-faced double pyramid (octohedron) of diamond, or the cube of rock salt, has not merely a peculiar external configuration, but an equally peculiar internal structure. That such is the case may be easily proved.

One of the most familiar and interesting crystals is a rhomb of Iceland or calcareous spar, one of the forms of crystallised carbonate of lime or chalk. It has a highly characteristic shape, distinguished by crystallographers as rhomboidal or rhombohedral, *i.e.*, rhomb-faced or lozenge-faced, because all its flat sides or faces, which are six in number, have the outline of the heraldic lozenge, or the diamond on a playing card. These six lozenge faces are bounded by sharply defined, unvarying angles.

But the spar crystal is something more than a mere shape. A plaster bust has externally the configuration of a human head, but the resemblance ceases within a line of the surface. You could not by examining a portion of the powder scraped from the back of the bust or the bottom of the pedestal, tell that it had been a bust, or what it had been ; and if the bust be broken, by, for example, a fall, the fragments have nothing in structure in common with the mere surface. So also an apple or a rose, modelled in wax, or a grape blown in glass, may completely deceive the eye, and, so far as form and colour are concerned, be mistaken for a real fruit or flower, but the resemblance ends with the outside.

On the other hand, if a crystal of calcareous spar be broken by a fall or a tap with a hammer, it breaks into rhombs, each with its six lozenge faces a perfect miniature copy of the original crystal, and those small rhombs may be broken by a gentle force into smaller rhombs, and these again into smaller, till the fragments, without varying their shape, become microscopically small. The Iceland spar thus resembles a house built of very small bricks all alike, or a piece of colourless mosaic where all the portions are identical, or a piece of marquetrie or Tunbridge wood-ware, consisting of exactly similar squares.

Further, an Iceland spar crystal has long been famous for its exhibition of the double refraction of light, *i.e.*, for its power to split into two a ray of light which falls upon it in any but a single direction, so as to double the image of every object seen through it ; and if one of these doubly refracted and, in conse-

quence, polarised rays be sent through such a crystal in any direction but one, it produces a curious array of black and white crosses and of beautifully coloured rings.

Now, the crystal thus endowed may have its salient angles knocked away, and any external configuration given to it without depriving it of those endowments. It may be carved into a square block or turned in a lathe into a sphere, and still it will break into lozenge-faced rhombs ; still it will refract light doubly ; still it will show crosses and prismatic rings when illuminated by a doubly refracted or polarised ray of light ; still it will conduct heat, according to the law that regulates conduction of heat by the unmutilated crystal ; still it will obey a magnet (diamagnetically) as if it were a perfect rhomboid.

All crystals more or less exhibit the same unity of structure. All are crystals in the atom as well as crystals in the mass. Through their height and depth and length and breadth, from their centre to their circumference, they are crystals ; and you no more change their inner and essential characters by changing their outer configuration, than you change a yew-tree into a church steeple by cutting it into the shape of a pyramid, or a box-tree into a bird by clipping it into the form of a peacock.

The crystalline structure is one which the glass-maker dreads, because the most important properties of glass are lost if it crystallise, and it greatly tends to crystallise. Yet, strangely enough, it is not that a crystal would not rival glass, for rock-crystal is better than glass for lenses and prisms : it is that we cannot produce *one* mighty glass crystal, out of which, like a great iceberg or ice-field, to saw windows, and chisel goblets, and carve lamps and looking-glasses, lenses and prisms. We are in this respect like men to whom some hundred acorns have been given, and who, if they had their will, would grow the hundreds into a single mighty oak, out of which might be sawn logs fit to form in one piece the keel or deck of a man-of-war, but who are compelled to accept a mere copsewood of many trees, and, in despair of oak, build their ships of fir and iron.

When glass crystallises it does not do so in one clear mass, but shoots up like an underwood into a forest of crystals ; and how incompatible this arrangement is with the employment of glass as a transmitter of light, any one may judge from the dimness of a window covered by a tree-like crystallisation of frost.

Glass, then, must not be crystalline. As little must it be amorphous. This word amorphous is not a technical one, for which technology need apologise; but it is a scientific one, and I use it because I know no everyday word which conveys its meaning. To speak of a solid body which presents to our eyes a visible, conspicuous shape, and a well-marked form, as shapeless and formless, seems on first consideration a foolish and contradictory thing. It is like speaking of a shapeless shape. Yet the language of poetry and the language of everyday life equally acknowledge the necessity of thus characterising certain indefinable forms. Thus Milton, in a famous passage of ' Paradise Lost,' describes Death as

' The other shape,
If shape it might be called, that shape had none
Distinguishable in member, joint, or limb;
Or substance might be called that shadow seemed,
. For each seemed either.'

Here we have the two essentials of amorphism, externally, vague outline, internally, vague structure. And if we at once descend from poetical altitudes, we shall find in the homely word *jelly* the occurrence of these amorphic essentials as fully recognised as in Milton's picture of Death. All are familiar with what a cook or confectioner calls a 'shape of jelly,' as a very visible, tangible, and withal beautiful solid. Yet think of that other most sad use of the word as applied to the utter annihilation of the perfection and beauty of a sensitive, living, graceful human body, when it is spoken of as the victim of some railway collision, or other terrible catastrophe, and is described as having been crushed or beaten into a jelly. We know that it retains a shape, but one so ill-defined that we speak of it as shapeless. In the same sense, the endlessly altering, undulating sea-Medusæ are popularly called jelly-fishes.

The other familiar amorphous bodies which I might name are, on the one hand, such soft substances as the curd of milk, the boiled white of egg, or clay in its plastic state as used by the potter and the sculptor; and on the other, such shapeless hard masses as flints or other silicious pebbles. In their internal structure, the softer of those bodies have an arrangement of particles approaching in mobility and unfixity to that of liquids; and the harder of the amorphous bodies exhibit none of the distinctive properties of crystals, and may be compared to congealed or rather coagulated jellies.

The only everyday English word which I have been able to think of as expressive of this formless form of matter is one which, from its associations, is perhaps not a very welcome one—namely, the word 'clot.' Clotted (or clouted) cream has no unpleasant associations with it, but one cannot say the same of clotted blood. Both, however, convey the same idea of vaguely consolidated substance; and I do not know a more significant phrase for solid sense apparently jumbled, till it has seemingly lost, though in reality it retains solidity, than the words of an old writer, applied by a reviewer of Thomas Carlyle to his 'Sartor Resartus,' as a book consisting of 'clotted nonsense.' The amorphous, curdled, or clotted condition, is as alien to the useful properties of glass as the crystallised one.

What, then, is the glassy shape or structure? It is a compromise between the crystalline and the amorphous one. Glass reflects and transmits light as a crystal does, but without necessarily doubly refracting or polarising it. It does not break into flat-faced, sharp-cornered solids like a crystal, but into curved or hollowed pieces, scooped out like shells; and when struck, as with a hammer, or allowed to fall, it is fractured into all kinds of curvilinear solids without shattering into acute-angled fragments or keen-edged grains.

You may be disposed to say that broken glass is sharp and cutting enough; and so, no doubt, it is, especially when the glass was originally thin; but look at the relics of a broken tumbler not deliberately ground to powder, and you will see that the sharpest pieces are rounded in their fracture. I have in my possession part of a glass air-pump receiver, crushed in by the pressure of the atmosphere; part of a soda-water glass machine, blown to pieces in my class-room; as well as the fragments of a glass basin, which spontaneously split in two. All display the same curved and waving outline, and, though sharp enough to hurt, are blunted on their edges. This waving, sinuous line is closely related to a property of glass, which connects it with the most glass-like of the amorphous bodies—viz., the jellies. If we take animal jelly or gelatine; for example, thick liquid isinglass or glue, we can draw it out into threads, and mould it into pliant shapes. But it is too semi-liquid in character, too unsolid, to admit of being condensed into permanent forms. Glass, however, at a certain stage in its passage from the perfectly liquid to the perfectly solid form, has this jelly-like or viscous plasticity, so that it may be run into moulds, spun into gossamer threads, blown into bubbles, drawn into

tubes, rolled out and stamped as if it were dough, clipped with scissors, pared with knives, squeezed, twisted, compressed, dilated, pulled out, pushed in, patched, puckered, smoothed, and welded, as if it were a ball of softened India-rubber or steam-hot gutta percha; whilst, in addition, glass finally settles or consolidates into a mass of stone-like hardness, which may be broken but will not bend.

Glass, then, has the following characters:—1. A brilliant lustre, which in other bodies we call the glassy lustre; 2. A shell-like or conchoidal, curved fracture; 3. A jelly-like plasticity, when passing from its liquid to its solid condition. Its particles are not marshalled together in the same rigidly harmonious way that the particles of crystals are, neither are they grouped or piled on one another, in the irregular fashion which characterises coagulated or amorphous masses; but it is impossible to give a precise definition of the internal structure of glass. In our ordinary language we restrict the word glass to a very few silicious compounds, but this is a merely conventional restriction. Thus, the simple combustibles phosphorus, sulphur, and carbon (as the diamond), can put on all the characters of glass. Many acids and their salts, such as phosphoric, boracic, and silicic acid, do the same. So do metallic oxides, such as oxide of lead, and many vegetable products, such as the gums, resins, and sugars.

All bodies possessing the characters named above constitute glass, whatever their nature or composition may be; and as the glassy or vitreous state and structure are intermediate between the amorphous and the crystalline one, so all kinds of glass are liable, on the one hand, to degenerate, as it were, into shapeless amorphism, or, on the other, to develop into symmetrical crystallinity. For example, the brilliantly combustible phosphorus, which we believe to be a simple or elementary substance, exhibits in its ordinary form, as melted and preserved under water, the glassy structure. But if we keep it long melted at a comparatively low heat, it becomes a crystalline mass, showing sometimes perfect twelve-sided, lozenge-faced crystals (rhombic dodecahedrons), like those of garnet. Again, if we keep it long heated, at a comparatively high temperature, it ceases to be either vitreous or crystalline, and becomes totally amorphous.

In like manner, sulphur may be procured in large, brilliant, beautifully transparent crystals; and also by heating to a certain point and suddenly cooling, as a glass which long retains plasticity and pliancy; and further by protracted heating and subsequent irregular cooling, as an uncrystalline, unvitreous mass.

The gums, resins, inspissated balsams, and other exudations from trees, along with amber, oscillate as it were between the glassy and amorphous conditions, being generally glassy, sometimes amorphous, and, most rarely of all, crystalline. No substance, however, exhibits the contrast between at least the vitreous and the crystalline condition, and the ready transition from the one to the other, better than sugar. Sugar, as it occurs in brown sugar, or in a sugar-loaf, or, still better, in sugar-candy, is one of the most perfectly crystallised bodies. Keep that sugar for some time melted, and it changes into a glass, and hardens as such. If you give a piece of it to a child as a plaything, and tell it that it is glass, sugar-glass, or vitreous sugar, it will smile at you and tell you it is not glass, but barley-sugar; and so it is, but none the less glass! It has all the essential properties of glass.

Lastly, the great ingredient of household glass, silica, can easily assume the crystalline, the vitreous, or the amorphous condition; and as it transfers this property to all the kinds of glass containing it, the glass-maker is often hard put to it, to keep the happy mean between amorphous shapelessness and crystalline symmetry. Thus, the most beautiful pyramid of colourless quartz, of purple amethyst, or yellow cairngorm, may be uncrystallised and changed into glass simply by being melted. It is true that no ordinary fire or even seven times heated furnace will melt such crystals, nor any artificial heat easily procurable, except that produced by the burning together of the elements of water, hydrogen, and oxygen ; but under this heat the hardest crystals of quartz melt into glass.

Electricity also can furnish a heat sufficient to effect this result, and it is seen on the grandest scale when thunder-storms send their discharges into beds of pure sand, and the white hot lightning melts its grains into glass. Tubes thus made in a moment out of lightning-melted sand, may be seen in the British and Jermyn Street Museums in London, and are justly reckoned objects of great interest and value.

And if it be possible to uncrystallise rock crystal into glass, it is still more easy to change both the rock crystal and its glass into amorphous, structureless silica. To do this it is only necessary to expose either to the vapour of the corroding hydrofluoric acid which fluorspar gives out when wetted with strong sulphuric acid. The crystal or the glass equally changes into a pulpy, gelatinous, starchy mass, which dries up like gum and hardens like glue. Chalcedony, common and precious opal, perhaps flint, jasper, and agate, are examples of this.

The glass-maker has thus a difficult task. Phosphorus, or sulphur, or barley-sugar, will scarcely do as the materials of window-panes and drinking glasses ; and lightning is an unmanageable servant. Our actual glass is in larger part silica, that it may be a clear, bright, transparent, insoluble, incorrodible, solid, enduring thing. But to secure its melting under our ordinary furnace heats, alkali, namely, soda or potash, is added, which renders it fusible and diminishes its tendency to crystallise ; and to give back to it the solid enduringness and insolubility in liquids which the alkali diminishes, infusible earths and heavy metallic oxides are added.

Thus window glass is made of the whitest sand melted with the cheapest alkali, soda, and hardened by lime ; but as soda colours glass green, flint-glass has potash instead of soda ; and as neither of these alkalies nor lime confers the greatest brilliancy upon glass, oxide of lead is added to the sand and potash, when the sparkle which we love to see in decanters and lamp shades and lustres is desired ; and by largely employing this lead oxide, the lenses and prisms suitable for the optician, and passable imitations of the gems are produced, whilst small additions of other metallic oxides give those beautiful colours which add such glory to cathedral windows. According to some, we have lost the secret of the ancient glass dyes ; but this is a mistake. Gold is as willing as of old to stain glass ruby red, and so is the humbler copper, which can also tincture it green. Silver secures a yellow or an orange, and iron gives the same. Cobalt provides for blue, copper and chromium for green, manganese for purple, and uranium for a topaz-like canary yellow. Tin makes a white glass milky and opaque, such as we see in the dials of watches ; and a black enamel is secured by the darker oxides of manganese, iron, and cobalt. Bottle glass is the humblest product of the glassy materials. Brown sand, spent lime, soapers' waste, clay, and common salt, are resolved by the furnace into a dark glass, which, if only cast into more graceful forms, would be as useful as it is without offending the eye.

The glass-maker's work, however, does not end when his vessels are fashioned into shape by dexterous manipulation of its substance when pliant and plastic.

They are in the highest degree fragile as they first leave his hands, so that they scarcely endure touching, and often fall to pieces. This fragility is owing chiefly to the different amount of extension and contraction which different parts of the glass have undergone whilst being fashioned into vessels, and to the unequal cooling of the deeper, as compared with the more superficial layers of the substance which have been more exposed to the cold external air in certain manipulations, and to the hot air of the furnace in others. A plastic mass like glass contracts most where it is most cooled, and least where it is least cooled. It thus resembles to some extent a web of woven tissue, such as a sail-cloth where some of the threads are pulled so tight as to be on the verge of breaking, whilst others are hanging in curves with no strain upon them at all. Such a piece of cloth is easily torn, for when pulled or stretched it does not resist with the united tenacity of all its threads, but only with that of the overstrained fibres, which quickly give way. If all the threads were equally tight, and the strain borne by them all, the web which before could be rent by the hands might, as the storm-sail of a man-of-war, withstand the fiercest hurricane.

Now, in the case of glass the unequally strained threads or fibres which make it up are afforded the opportunity of lengthening or shortening themselves till they are of the same length, by heating the completed vessels or other articles of glass up to the temperature at which it begins to soften, but no higher (otherwise they would lose their shape and symmetry), and then allowing it very slowly to cool down to the temperature of the air. Glass for choice optical purposes is thus allowed to fall gradually from a high to a low temperature through the space of many days, and in all cases hours are allowed to elapse during the cooling. This process is called annealing. Shakspere introduces a most expressive figurative use of it, strikingly bringing out its meaning, when he makes Hamlet's father denounce his murderer for hurrying him into the world of spirits—

'Un-anneal-d;
No reckoning made, but sent to my account
With all my imperfections on my head '

In other words, unprepared to endure unscathed the powers of so dread a place.

It is exceedingly probable that in the glass-maker's annealing process there is not merely an equable mechanical arrangement of the glass particles in the way mentioned, but also a combination of heat with them, which is another element of stability. We know, for example, that when cold iron and other metals are long hammered, they give out so much heat as even to become red-hot ; but at the same time, they grow brittle and lose malleability, and the only way in which this brittleness can be removed, and malleability restored to them, is by heating them red-hot and allowing them slowly to cool. During this process, these metals apparently recover and render latent within their substance the heat which is essential to their solidity ; and in the same way glass appears to require and to obtain, during the process of annealing, an amount of heat essential to its stability. At all events, annealing renders glass, which otherwise would be uselessly brittle, wonderfully strong and enduring, as the immense window-panes and mirrors which can now be cast in plate-glass strikingly exhibit ; and not less the comparatively thin tubes employed by the chemist, which he is not afraid to expose to a pressure of several hundred pounds upon each square inch. Let us now consider glass as illustrating the objects with which an Industrial Museum has to do.

An Industrial Museum is intended to be a repository for all the objects of useful art, including the raw materials with which each art deals, the finished products into which it converts them, drawings and diagrams explanatory of the processes through which it puts those materials, models or examples of the machinery with which it prepares and fashions them, and the tools which specially belong to it, as a particular craft. Such a museum should also include illustrations of the progress of each industrial art from age to age; of its dependence on the sister arts, and the extent to which it ministers to them; of its relation to the products of our own country, and to those of foreign lands; of the amount of wealth which it consumes, circulates, and produces; of its healthfulness as a vocation for the different sexes and ages; of its relation to good morals, and the service which it can render the State by employing the needy, increasing the comforts of the poor, advancing the civilisation of all classes, adding to the material, intellectual, and moral prosperity of the whole nation, and, through it, more or less of the entire world.

Now, instead of attempting a formal catalogue of all the arts which would thus be represented in an Industrial Museum, let us be content on this occasion to see how it would deal with glass in the several relations referred to. In the first place, then, the museum itself might be built of glass, like the Industrial Palace at Hyde Park in 1851, or the present Palace at Sydenham. The raw materials of glass, arranged in due order, would directly connect the museum with distant regions of the globe, and with men of various nations, and of still more various professions. Thus, the sand used in glass-making is brought to Scotland from the Isle of Wight, from North and South America, and from Australia. The soda comes in part from our northern and western shores, in part from Spain and the Levant, in part from the natron lakes of Egypt: but most of the soda is made in our own country, by a complex chemical process from common salt, which involves the consumption of ship-loads of sea-salt from different parts of the world, of ship-loads of sulphur dug up in Sicily, of ship-loads of chalk or limestone quarried in England, and of ship loads and truck-loads of coal mined in our coal districts.

The potash of flint glass is extracted from wood ashes for us by the Americans, Canadians, and Russians. The lead of our flint glass is mined and smelted in Lanarkshire, Dumfriesshire, and Cumberland. The manganese, used both to bleach and to give a purple colour to glass, is brought from England, Spain, America, and the Continent. The copper used in staining it green, and the tin for white enamel, come from Cornwall. The cobalt, so extensively employed in colouring glass blue, is imported from the Saxon mines or from those in the mountains of Norway. The silver which stains glass yellow and orange may be from Transylvania, Chili, or Peru, and the gold which makes it ruby red, from California. There is thus a whole fleet of ships, and an entire battalion of sailors, engine-drivers, railway porters, colliers, quarrymen, miners, metal workers, and others waiting on the glass-maker.

Again, the glass-work must be very carefully built by the mason and bricklayer, and the potter must exercise his greatest skill in furnishing suitable pots in which to melt the glass, and the brick-maker his skill in providing suitable fire bricks for the furnaces.

Machinery also is needed to grind and mix the materials, and to move the glass-cutting wheels, as well as for other purposes, so that the mill-wright and mechanician, the engineer and carpenter, must lend their aid.

Again, the tools employed in fashioning glass are chiefly of iron, and the smith is needed for them; nor will I detain you further by enumerating one by one the chemist to analyse, the artist to design, the managers, financiers, and multitude of unskilled labourers who must be connected with a glass-work. I might, I think, without expending any overplus of ingenuity, bring in all the other craftsmen under the wing of the glass-maker, and if restricted by my superiors to the illustration in the Industrial Museum only of glass-making, could include under that art all other arts, because they are needful to it, as it is to them. But my present motive in speaking thus is to make all perceive how full of profit, interest, and instruction an Industrial Museum could not but be to every honest, open-eyed visitor, no matter what his or her rank, vocation, tastes, or sympathies were, provided only there was some love of mankind in the heart, and some power of perception acting through the brain.

Take this matter of glass in proof thereof. Under what immeasurable obligations are all sections of mankind to the glass-maker, and with what interest should we study the properties of glass. But for the glass-maker, astronomy would now be but little advanced beyond its condition in the days of the Chaldean shepherds; and in cloudy climates like our own, the great Newtons, and Hookes, Flamsteeds, and Herschels, who have triumphed by their optical instruments over all the gloom of our sullen heavens, would have abandoned to the lonely herdsman under cloudless eastern skies, a science forbidden to them, or would have wasted their days in vain wishes that they had been called like David to follow upon Syrian hills 'the ewes great with young.'

But for the glass-maker, optics would be but the shadow of what it is. The telescope, the microscope, and the prism might never have been, and we might still be profoundly ignorant of the wonderful properties of light, and literally walking in darkness.

But for the glass-maker, the chemist would have remained an anomalous compound of the cook and the blacksmith, boiling and distilling in opaque vessels, through whose walls nothing could be seen, and blinding himself by staring into a furnace, where the changes which its heat was producing on substances exposed to its flames could not be traced otherwise than most imperfectly. Chemistry may, in truth, so far as the greater part of it is concerned, be defined as the 'science of the glass vessel.'

Natural philosophy, however, is scarcely less indebted than chemistry to the wonderful properties of glass. But for the glass-maker, there would be no transparent air pump, and, as a result, no satisfying knowledge of the air, and only a maimed and imperfect science of pneumatics and the gases.

But for the glass-maker, there would be no transparent barometer or thermometer, and meteorology would now be a science crippled from birth, and halting on both feet.

But for the glass-maker, we should have had no glass electrical machine, and had that not been in our hands for more than a hundred years, we should still be far distant from electric telegraphs, electric lights, electro-metallurgy, or lightning-conductors.

But for the glass-maker, we should have had no photography, and that most faithful of all artists, the sun, would still in vain be offering us the command of the pencil, which he had in vain been offering to the generations which preceded us for thousands of years.

But for the glass-maker, the botanist could never have tempted the palm trees and bananas, the passion-flowers and camellias, the grapes and melons, and pine-apples of more sunny lands, to migrate to our cold island, and defy its rigours under a sky of glass; and he would have had no microscope to reveal to him the hidden marvels of their beautiful structure.

But for the glass-maker, the zoologist could not, as he now can, even though far inland, study better than even at the sea-side all the habits of the rarest and most fragile sea-creatures, and watch through the walls of their glass prison the ever-changing phenomena of their strange life.

But for the glass-maker, the anatomist would still, like the botanist, be without his microscope, and the knowledge which it has given him of the structures of the body; nor could he, as he does, preserve in transparent vessels, for detailed study by himself and others, those curious organs which it his delight to unfold.

Such are some of the obligations of science to glass; but it is not theoretical science alone that is indebted to the glass-maker. The sailor on the outlook, the mariner doubtful of his latitude, the sentinel at his post, the engineer planning a siege, the general guiding a battle, the surveyor mapping out the globe, the engraver, the watchmaker, and many another practicist on the great and small scale are beholden to the glass of their telescopes, sextants, theodolites, and magnifying lenses for the success, not to say the perfection of their arts. The health and beauty of the whole community are ministered to by the large modern transparent window, the glass lamp-shade, and glass drinking-vessel, and its beauty is especially cared for by the modern looking-glass.

It is curious, indeed, to see how many useful objects appropriate to themselves as sufficiently distinctive, the one word 'glass.' The thirsty man calls his drinking-vessel a glass. The sailor looks out for his land-marks with a glass. The beauty gazes into a glass. Best of all, the otherwise blind man, grateful to the special artist we are praising for his gift (with reverence I use the words) of 'eyes to the blind,' calls his spectacles 'glasses.'

Lastly, if we do not yet see winter gardens domed with glass, where invalids may realise a Madeira at home, or, at least, throw away their respirators and be forgetful of the east wind, at all events we have our Crystal Palaces, which more than most human productions resemble divine ones, inasmuch as they are at once as perfect as mechanical works and pieces of engineering, as they are as works of beauty.

I rejoiced to hear my friend Professor Huxley protest from this rostrum against nature being criticised as a machine and not admired as a poem. The delightful thing is, that nature is both, so that when you are in an engineering turn of mind you can employ yourself to the full in demonstrating that the world is a great spinning top, a great clock, or a compensation pendulum, all of which it certainly is; and when you are in a poetical turn of mind you can feel that the world is a reflection of God, a work of high art by the highest artist, a great painting, and poem, and song, and sculpture in one.

And so, whilst in the Crystal Palace the lover of mathematical precision in squaring sheets of glass, and in piecing them together in multiples of the dimensions of each single sheet, and the delighted calculator of the proper length, breadth, and thickness of iron pillars, cross-ties, and girders, might enjoy himself to the full; the artist, blind to these things, which he could not see, though his eyes were open, might admire the beautiful result, for him as causeless as the glory of a flower, which nevertheless is realised in conformity with mathematical and numerical laws, as much more rigid than those observed in the construction of a Crystal Palace as the glory of a flower exceeds the glory of the grandest edifice that man can plan.

In speaking thus, I cannot forget that not long ago, from this very rostrum, glass buildings were condemned in your hearing, by the eloquent Oxford graduate, John Ruskin, who adduced something like a Scriptural anathema on building with anything but brick

and stone.* But surely Ruskin was wrong, for besides the 'sea of glass like unto crystal' which St John saw before the throne of God, and the 'sea of glass mingled with fire,' on which he beheld the redeemed standing, 'having the harps of God,' the Heavenly City is described by him as of 'pure gold like unto clear glass,' and 'the street of the city was pure gold, as it were transparent glass;' so that even, though we allow for a latitude in the interpretation of the term glass, as used by an ancient writer, still we must understand by it something solid, massive, transparent, and altogether unlike brick or stone, and may claim the sanction of one sacred author for buildings of glass.

But, however this may be, I feel that had I been privileged, as some of my friends were, to walk alone by midsummer twilight through the long aisles and arcades of the first and most famous Crystal Palace of 1851, I should not have paced its solitary courts without thinking of it as an emblem of this earth, with its overarching, half-revealing, half-concealing sky, or without remembering that St Paul, spanning by a divine standard the horizon of man's knowledge in all directions, declared that 'here we see through (or in) a glass darkly.' This earth is for the industrial man a transparent bee-hive; for the aesthetical man, a covered garden and green-house, full of flowers, and statues, and birds of song; for the scientific man, a dark diving-bell, with mere eyelets to admit the light, lying at the bottom of the ocean which he longs to explore; and for all men, however thin and invisible the walls at times may appear, it is a prison; and, as Shelley sang—

'Life, like a dome of many-coloured glass,
  Stains the white radiance of Eternity,
    Until Death tramples it to fragments.'

Such are some of the modes in which the glass objects collected in an Industrial Museum might instruct and interest its visitors, whatever their tastes or inclinations.

Pottery would have equally served to illustrate the idea and aims of such a museum. It takes its name from the word 'pot,' by which is generally understood a cooking-vessel; but in its earlier and quite innocent meaning it signified a drinking-vessel, and is connected with our terms potion and potation. The French have borrowed from the Greeks, and transferred to us the term Ceramic, to denote the art of the potter. If those philologists are right who derive this word from the ancient Hellenic name of a horn, i.e., a drinking horn, then potter's art and Ceramic art have exactly the same signification. But both these derivations, favoured by the French writers on the art under notice, are disallowed by our ablest English classical scholars. We have certainly from the Latin the term 'fictile' art in allusion to the great plasticity of unbaked clay.

Fictile is the best title, if we are to employ a foreign word not very familiar to all. This I am slow to do, but we have scarcely a choice, for no adjective is readily derivable from the word 'pottery,' whilst such an adjective is often needed.

The plasticity of wet clay is its characteristic property, and permits it to be moulded into all shapes. The potter from the oldest times has turned this to ample account by that very ancient machine, the potter's wheel, of which, did time permit, I could say much. I will only observe on the whole subject that keeping to our own old English word pottery, we include under it two things, namely, earthenware, i.e.,

* Lectures on Architecture and Painting, delivered at Edinburgh in November 1853. Lect. 1, pp. 60-62.

earth or clay (silicate of alumina), baked in the sun, or burned in the kiln; and China or Porcelain. The last word is said to be derived through the Portuguese, from the same Latin root which yields our English term pork. The Portuguese, after their discovery of the passage to the East round the Cape of Good Hope, brought the fictile productions of China, for the first time, largely to Europe. They called the material of those wares porcelain, from its surface and polish resembling those of certain shells belonging to the genus Cypræa, often seen on our mantelpieces, and familiar probably to all as represented by the common cowry. These shells they had long been in the habit of likening to young swine, and to them they also likened the porcelain cups, which they thought resembled them.

By a curious coincidence we have long been in the custom in Scotland of applying the term 'pig' to a stoneware vessel; a use of the word which surprises an Englishman, and still more an Irishman, but would probably please a Portuguese. Our Scotch term, which is not generally associated with the notion of an animal, is said to be of Celtic origin, but this seems scarcely reconcilable with its wide employment in our Lowlands, where I believe it is more familiar than in the Gaelic districts of the country. Be this as it may, we can find an expressive English term for China or porcelain. Earthenware is otherwise clay-ware, i.e., clay or crumbled felspar (silicate of alumina), thoroughly dried and intensely heated, but not fused or vitrified. Porcelain is clay-and-glass-ware, i.e., clay and vitreous matter (which may be of many kinds) incorporated, and heated till they are semifused into a mass, which combines the opaque rigidity and earthiness of the clay, with the transparency and elasticity of the glass. Between indurated earth, such as we have in a flower-pot and perfect glass, we may produce by suitable mixtures a very large number of intermediate 'wares,' admitting of almost endless modifications and of application to as many arts.

Under clay, and the alumina (oxide of aluminium) which occurs in it, large reference might be made to the applications of compounds of alumina in dyeing and pigment-making, but I must avoid these tempting technological subjects. Time will only allow me to make a reference to the metal of clay, aluminium. Take from the non-silicious earth (alumina), which is one of the two constituents of clay, its oxygen, and a metal remains, aluminium. It is most easily prepared from a beautiful mineral called cryolite from its resemblance to ice, and containing the metal united with sodium and fluorine. Aluminium is spoken of as rivalling silver in brilliancy; but those who wish it to pass for such would do well to recall what Caleb Balderstone said when he tried to make the polished pewter flagons of the Master of Ravenswood pass for plate—'I think it may do; I think it might pass, if they winna bring it ower muckle in the licht of the window.' Aluminium certainly more resembles tin or pewter than silver in lustre. Its better qualities are its little liability to tarnish, and consequent cleanliness, its great lightness, which places it for the present, so far as many useful purposes are concerned, above all the other metals, and its remarkable sonorousness, which gives it a peculiar value as a material for bells, gongs, and musical instruments. Should it hereafter be used instead of silver for table-services, it will be curious to consider how little at any time has been the difference between the poor man's stoneware platter and the rich man's plate. In the platter there are two metals united with oxygen, in the plate, one which is free. It is not improbable that the two metals in question, aluminium and silicium, will hereafter rival silver in economic if not in monetary value. But to such speculations of industrial science there is no end.

I have thus imperfectly endeavoured, in two hastily prepared lectures, to explain and illustrate the aim of Technology, and the object of Industrial Museums.

Allow me, in conclusion, to ask your good offices towards the Scottish Industrial Museum. A grant of money is at my disposal for the purchase of specimens; but it is small, and will not go far even in purchasing what can be purchased for money. But money alone will not procure many of the objects which it is most desirable to possess. These, even if paid for at market-price, will be furnished only by those who believe that an Industrial Museum will do an important service to the entire country, and are willing to assist in the good work.

I am especially anxious, in addressing this audience, to enlist the sympathies of intelligent women in its behalf. They can contribute the graceful works of their own hands, which form some of the most highly prized objects in the English and Irish museums, and they can persuade those of the rougher sex, who come within the sphere of their influence, to give or procure objects for the industrial collection. I entreat them to do so, if from no other motive than from this, that they may thereby contribute to increase the means of giving an industrial education to women of the poorer classes, and to multiply the vocations which may keep them from starvation, misery, and crime.

Printed by JOHN STEWART, Writers' Court, Royal Exchange, Edinburgh.